Puzzle Pals

50+ Festively Themed Step By Step Drawings

How To Draw
Christmas

Bryce Ross

How To Draw Christmas For Kids: 50+ Festively Themed Step By Step Drawings For Kids Ages 4 - 8

by Bryce Ross

ISBN: 978-1-990100-47-5

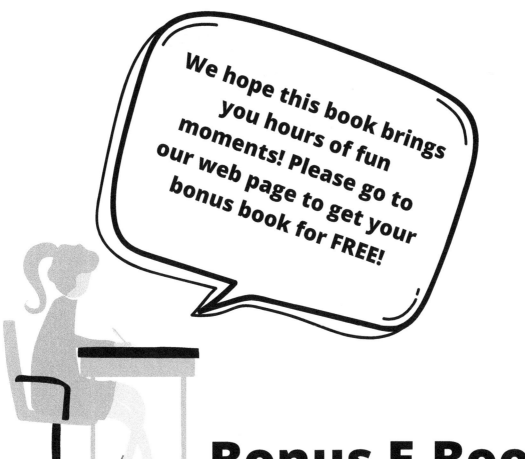

We hope this book brings you hours of fun moments! Please go to our web page to get your bonus book for FREE!

Bonus E-Book

www.puzzlepalsbooks.com/kids

7.99

Santa Clause

Practice

Polar Bear

Practice

Mouse King

Practice

Snowflakes

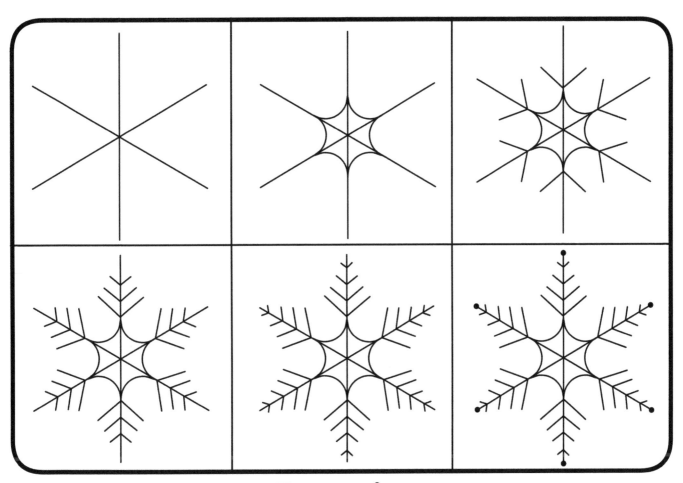

Practice

Penguin

Practice

Ballerina

Practice

Doves

Practice

Moose

Practice

Mountains

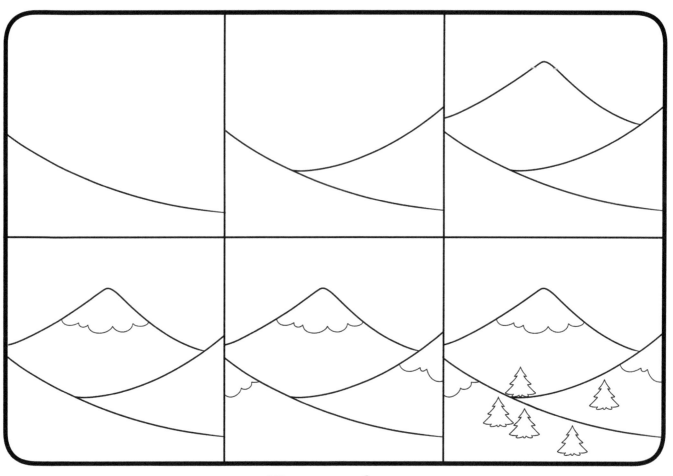

Practice

Nutcracker

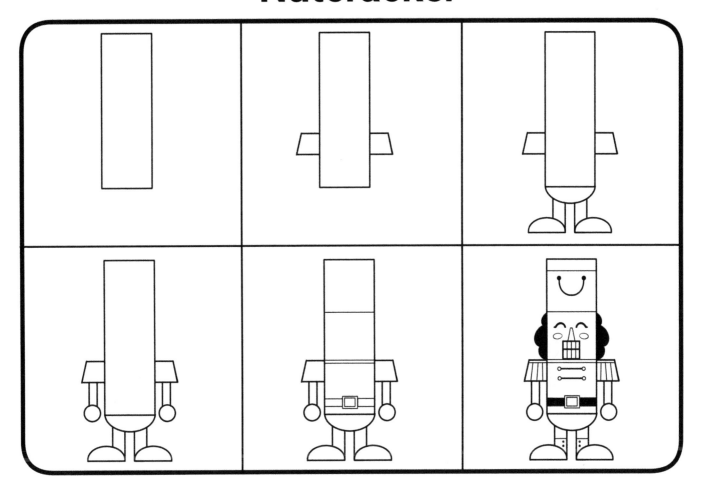

Practice

Snow Skier

Practice

Ice Skates

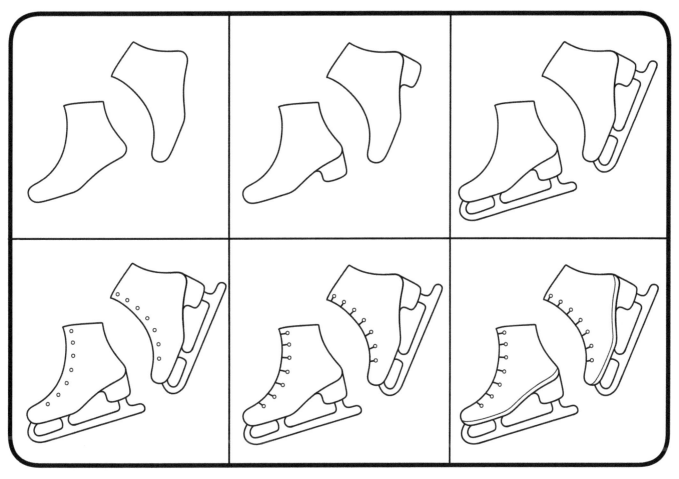

Practice

Mittens

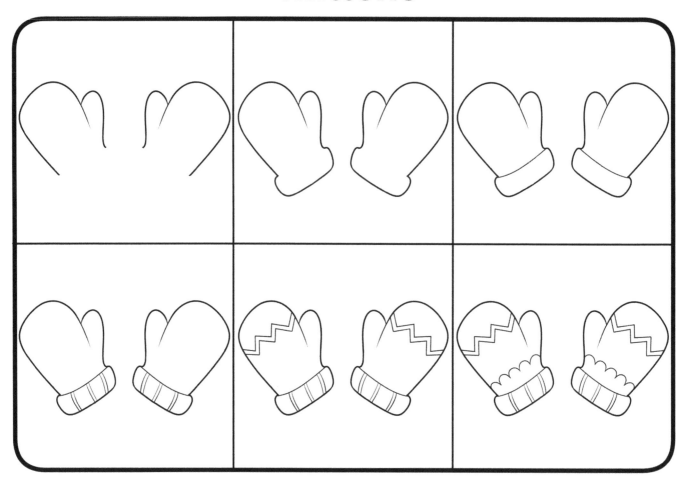

Practice

Toque

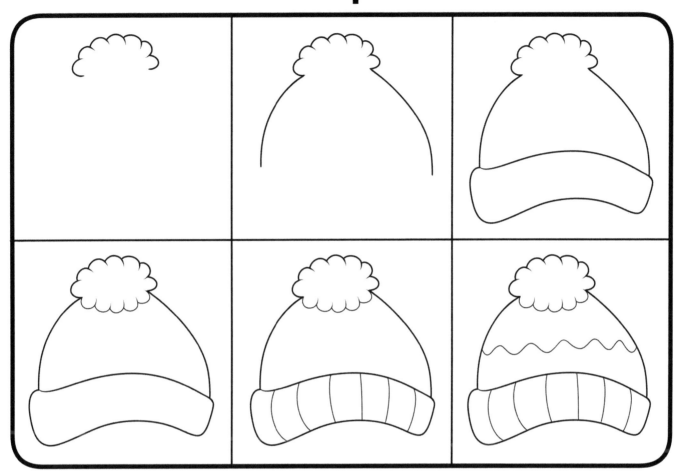

Practice

Snow Jacket

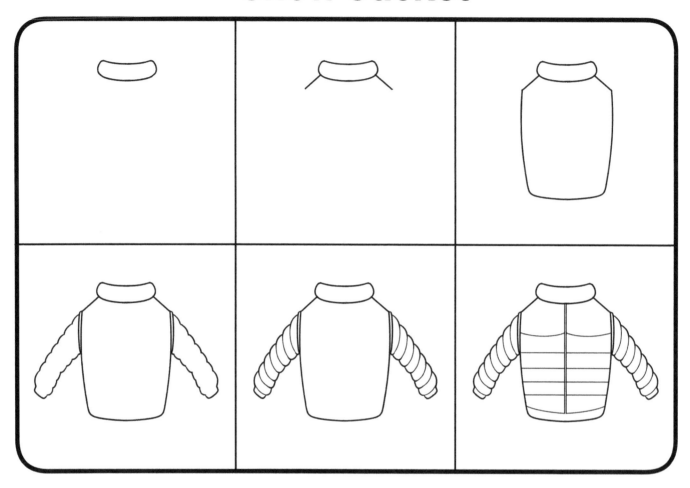

Practice

Jack in the box

Practice

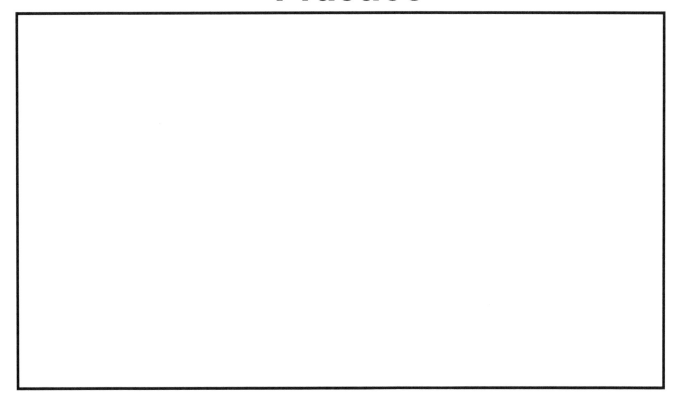

Reindeer

Practice

Sleeping

Practice

Santa's Sack

Practice

Christmas Puppy

Practice

Turkey

Practice

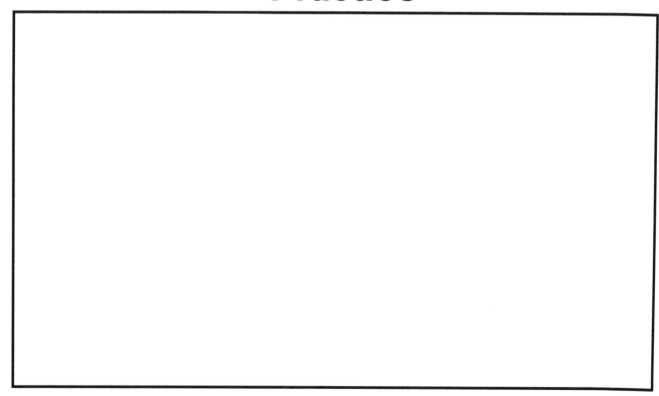

Angel

Practice

Gingerbread Woman

Practice

Gingerbread Man

Practice

Christmas Star

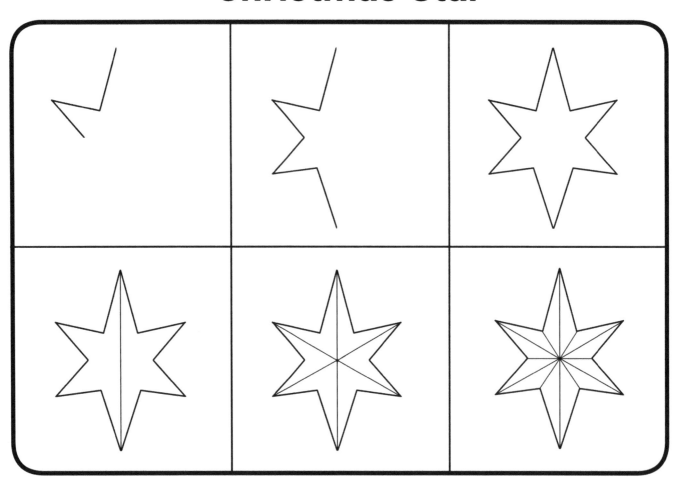

Practice

Bells

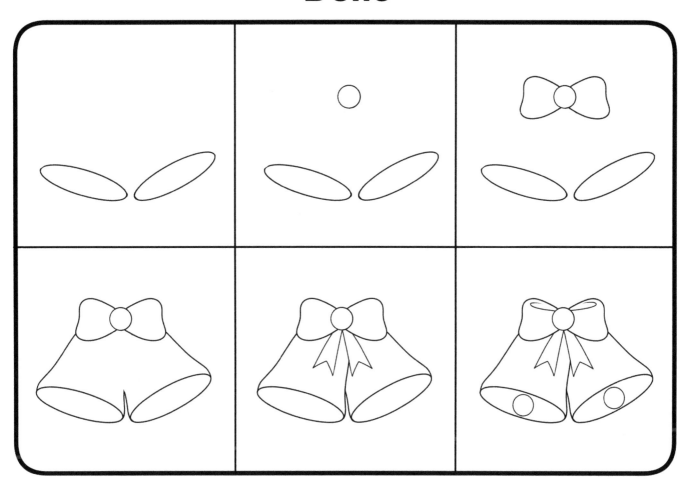

Practice

Toys

Practice

Snow Globe

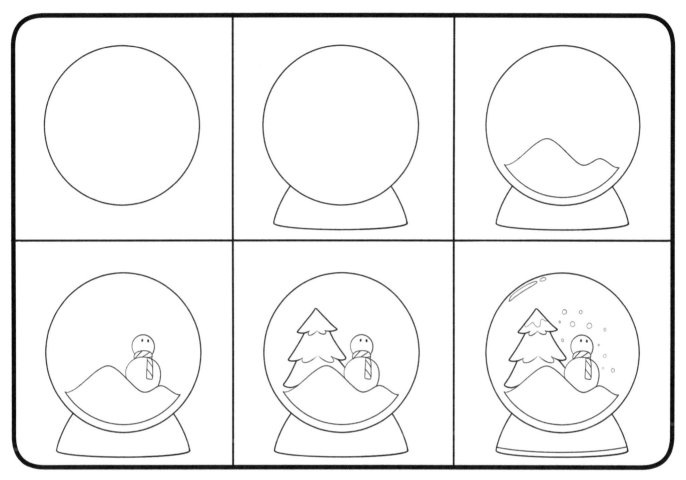

Practice

Christmas Hat

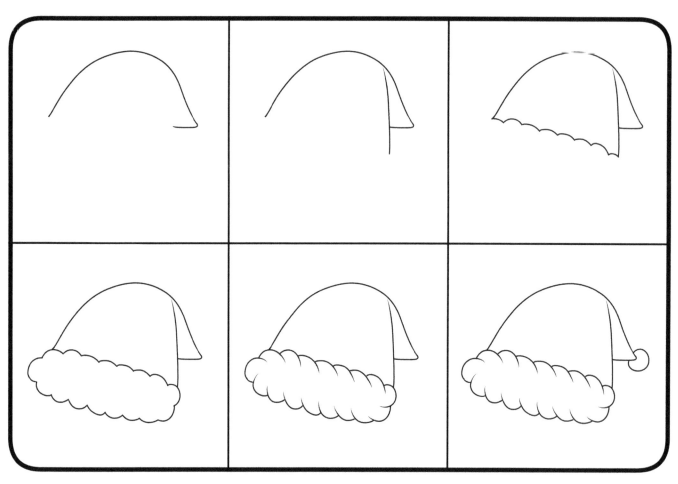

Practice

Snowman

Practice

Candle

Practice

Christmas Lights

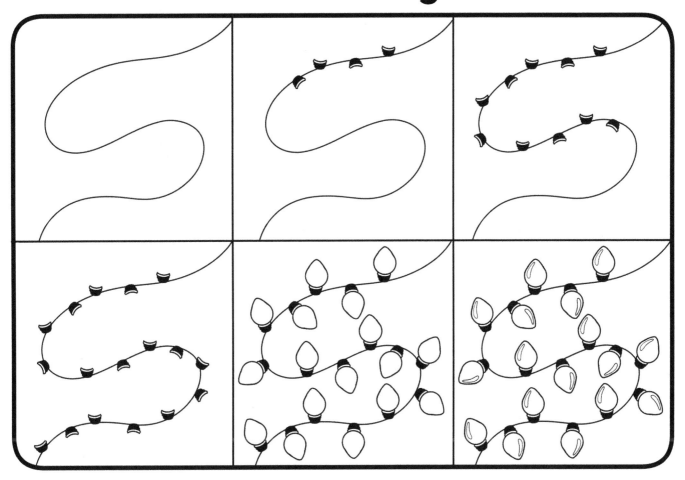

Practice

Chimney

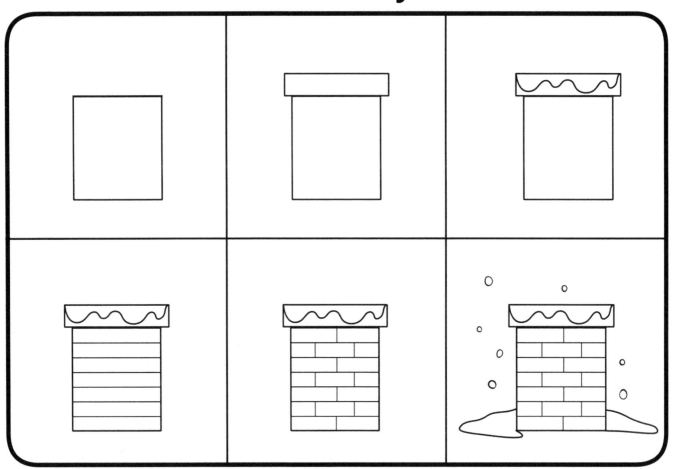

Practice

Chrismtas Caroler

Practice

Wreath

Practice

Cookies

Practice

Ornament

Practice

Girl Elf

Practice

Mrs. Clause

Practice

Boy Elf

Practice

Candy Cane

Practice

Stockings

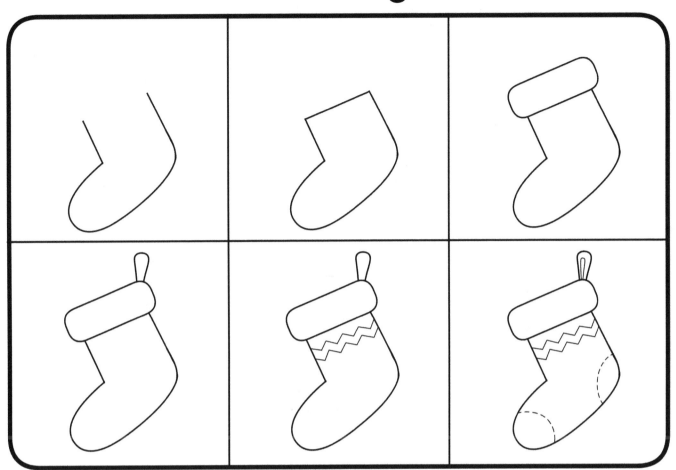

Practice

Presents

Practice

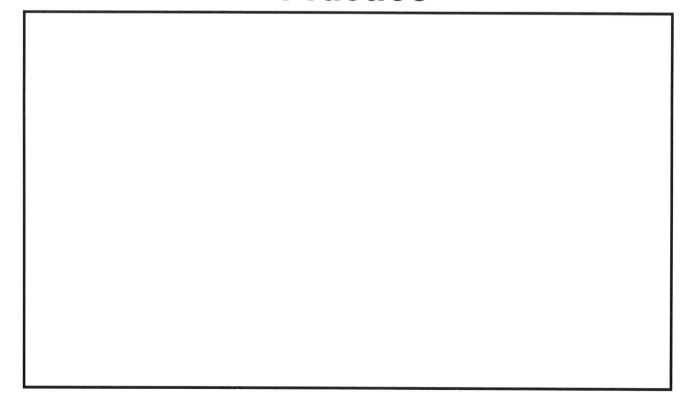

Abominable Snowman

Practice

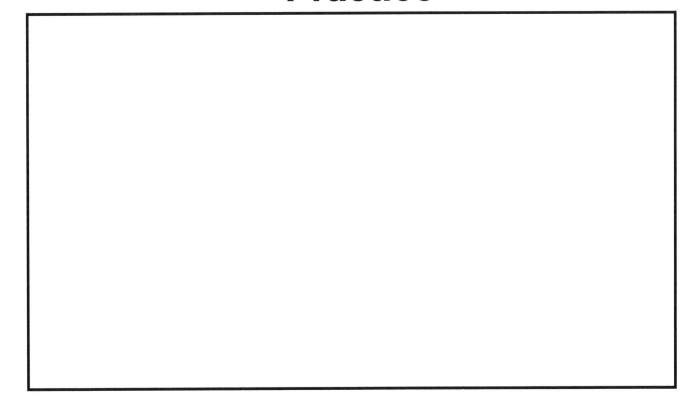

Mistletoe

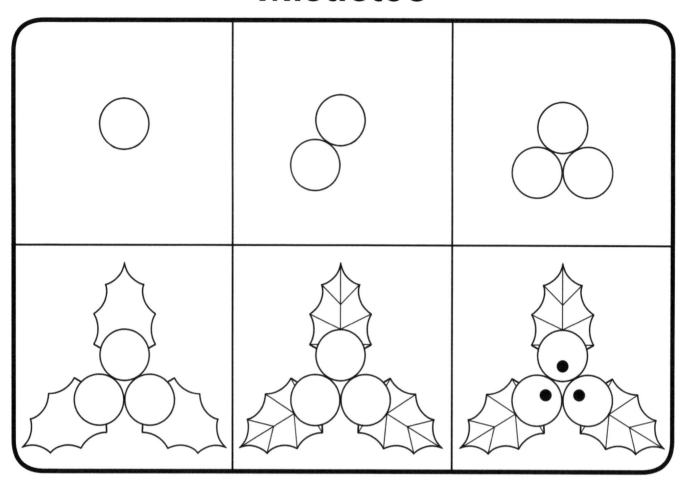

Practice

Santa's Sleigh

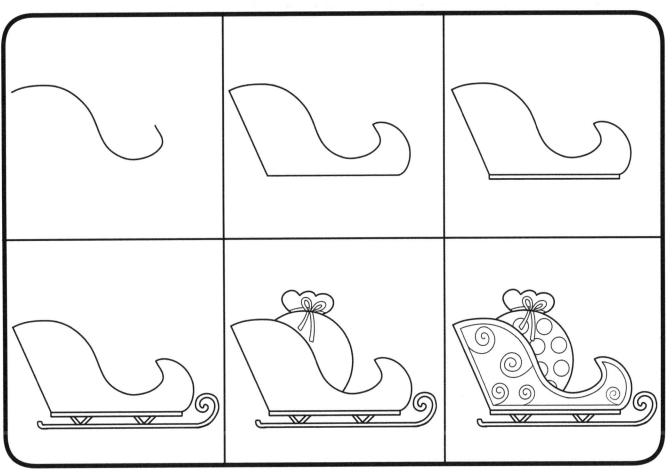

Practice

North Pole

Practice

Christmas Tree

Practice

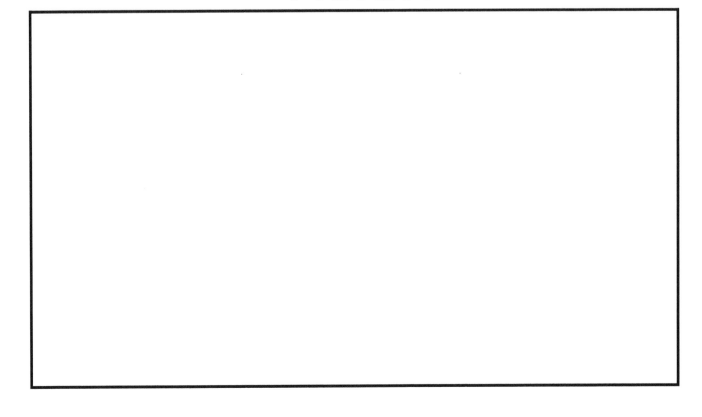

Gingerbread House

Practice

Christmas

Practice

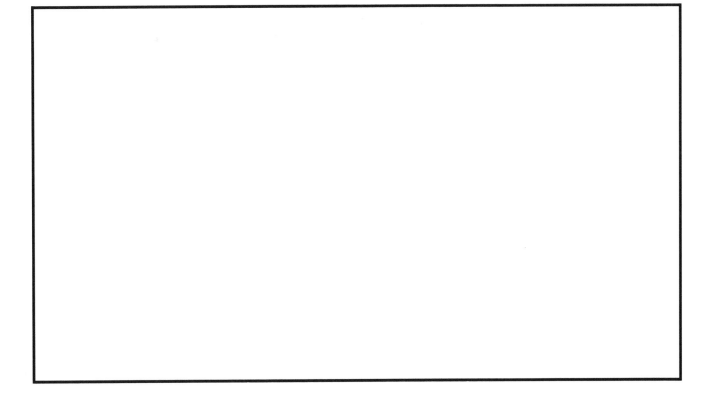

We hope this book brought you hours of fun moments! Please go to our web page to get your bonus book for FREE!

Bonus E-Book

www.puzzlepalsbooks.com/kids

7.99

WOULD YOU RATHER For Kids

HILARIOUS KIDS GAMES

Printed in the USA
CPSIA information can be obtained
at www.ICGtesting.com
LVHW081606111123
763605LV00004B/11